1 Light and shadow

Light energy

We see things when light from them enters our eyes.
Some objects make light and others reflect it.

Q1 Copy this table.

Look at the picture and then complete the table.

Object	Does not make light. It is seen when it relects light	Makes light by burning or by chemical reaction	Makes light from electricity
Street lights			✓

Shadows

A shadow is a dark area that light cannot get to.

In this experiment you will investigate how shadows are made.

Apparatus

☐ light source ☐ screen
☐ card ☐ scissors

Q1 Copy this table.

What was changed?	What happened to the shadow?

A Cut a cross shape out of the card. Use this to make a shadow on the screen. ▲

B Think of ways to change the size of the shadow.
1 Decide what to change.
2 Make the change.
3 Record what happens. ▲

Q2 List all the ways in which you can make the shadow bigger.

Q3 Does any light get to the screen behind the card?

Q4 What does this tell you about the way light moves? (This picture will give you a clue.)

Extension exercise 1 can be used now.

2 The pinhole camera

In a **pinhole camera** an **image** (picture) is made by straight rays of light from an object, passing through a small hole, onto the screen. In this experiment you will **investigate** how the camera works.

Q1 Copy this table.

Size of pinhole	Image – clear or blurred	Image – bright or dull	Image – upright or upside down
Small			
Large			

A Using a rubber band, fix some tracing paper to the open back of the pinhole camera. This will act as a screen. ▲

B Using the second rubber band, fix some sugar paper around the screen end of the camera. This acts as a shade for the screen. ▲

C Using a pin, make a small neat hole in the centre of the foil at the front of the camera. The camera is now ready. ▲

D Work in a darkened area. Point the pinhole end of the camera at the lamp. Look at the screen. ▲

E Move the camera nearer to, then further away from the lamp. Look at the image (picture) on the screen. ▲

F Use the pin to make the pinhole bigger. Repeat **E**. ▲

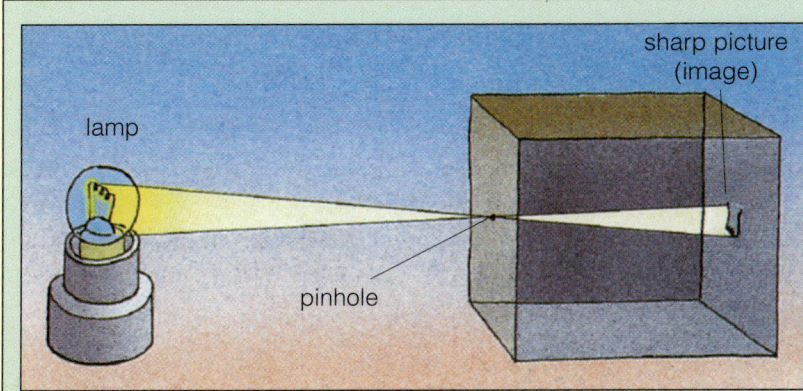

lamp

pinhole

sharp picture (image)

Q2 The diagram on the left shows how light from the lamp gets to the screen. Use it to help you explain why the image is always upside down.

Q3 What difference does it make to the image if you move the camera nearer the lamp?

Q4 Which size hole gives you the brighter image?

Q5 Why do you think this size of hole gives you the brighter image?

Extension exercise 2 can be used now.

Apparatus

☐ ray box ☐ power pack
☐ plain paper ☐ protractor
☐ mirror and support ☐ ruler

Mirrors

All objects **reflect** light – that is how we see them.

Mirrors reflect light in a special way because they are very flat and shiny. In this experiment you will find out how light is reflected by a mirror.

Q1 Copy this table.

Angle of incidence, i	Angle of reflection, r

B Shine a ray of light on to the mirror. If you can't see the ray coming out you will need to work in a darker area. Mark the rays of light with crosses. ▲

A Place the mirror on the paper. Draw a line along the back of the mirror. ▲

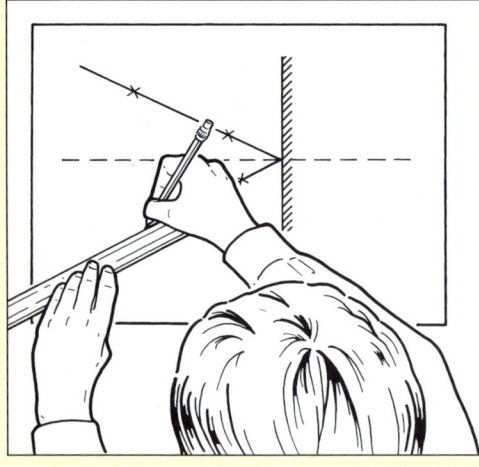

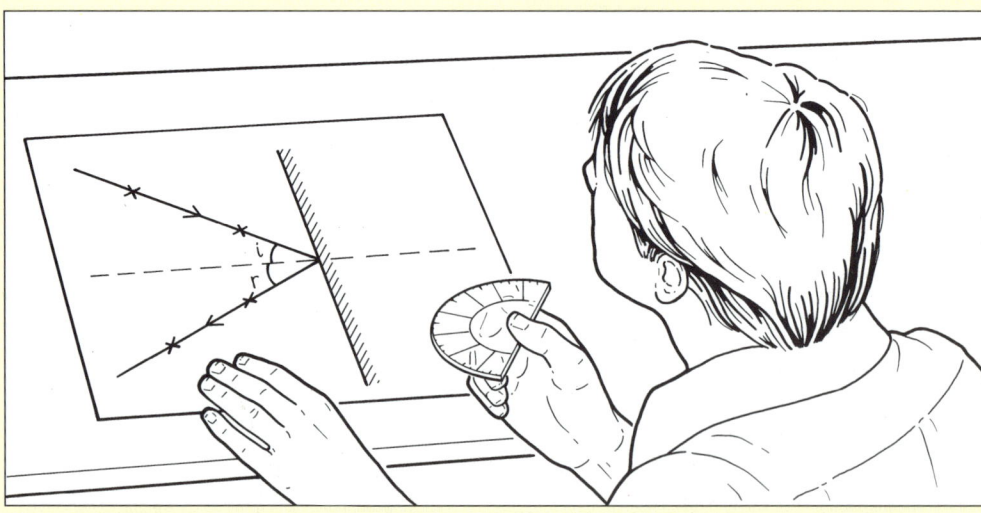

C Take away the mirror and ray box. Draw lines showing where the rays went. Use a protractor to draw a dotted line at right angles (90°) to the mirror. ▲

D Use a protractor to measure the angle the ray goes in at (**the angle of incidence, i**) and the angle it comes out at (**the angle of relection, r**) Write the results in the table. ▲

E Repeat **A**–**D** three more times, shining the light at different angles.

Q2 What did you find out about how the angle of reflection changed when you changed the angle of incidence?

Extension exercise 3 can be used now.

Finding the image

Let's investigate the picture (**image**) we see in a mirror.

Apparatus

☐ mirror and support ☐ 2 rulers
☐ optical pin ☐ Plasticine

A Place the mirror in the middle of the paper. Draw a line along the back of the mirror. ▲

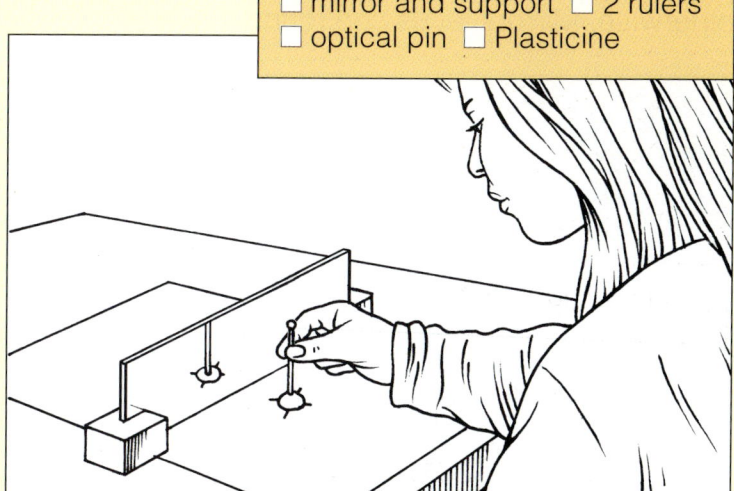

B Draw a cross on the paper in front of the mirror. Place the pin on the cross. ▲

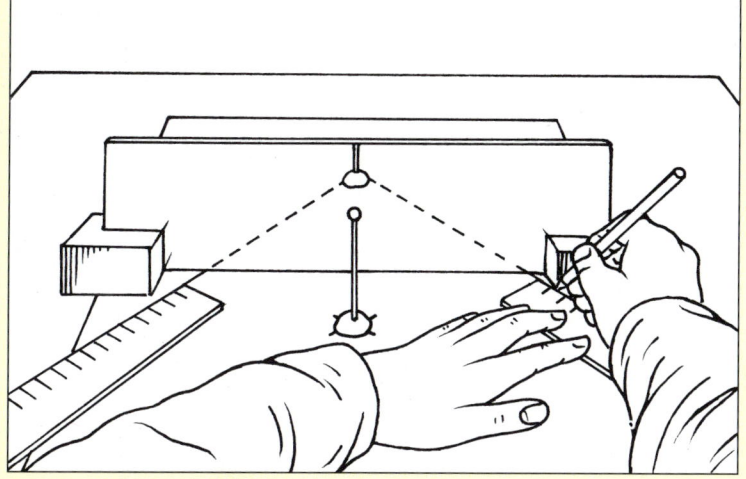

C Position the two rulers so that their outside edges point at the image of the pin. Draw along these edges. ▲

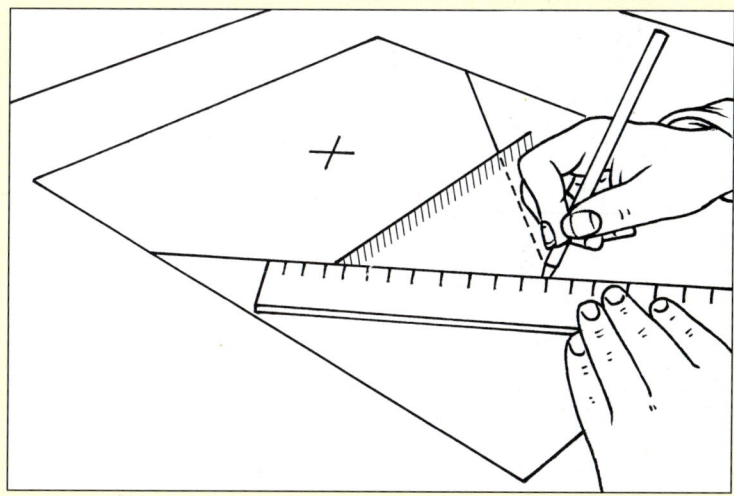

D Remove the pin and mirror. Continue the two lines until they meet. This is where the image was. Measure the distance from the pin to the mirror and the distance from the mirror to the image. ▲

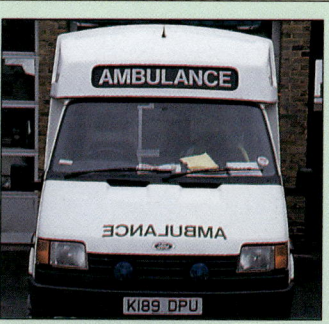

Q1 Is the image in front of, behind or on the mirror?

Q2 What did you notice about the two distances you measured?

Q3 Explain how reflection is being used in each of these photographs.

Extension exercise 4 can be used now.

Seeing around corners

Mirrors can help us to see things we wouldn't be able to see otherwise. Mirrors let us see round corners.

Apparatus

☐ 2 mirrors ☐ metre ruler
☐ Blu-Tack ☐ protractor
☐ cardboard tube
☐ sharp scissors

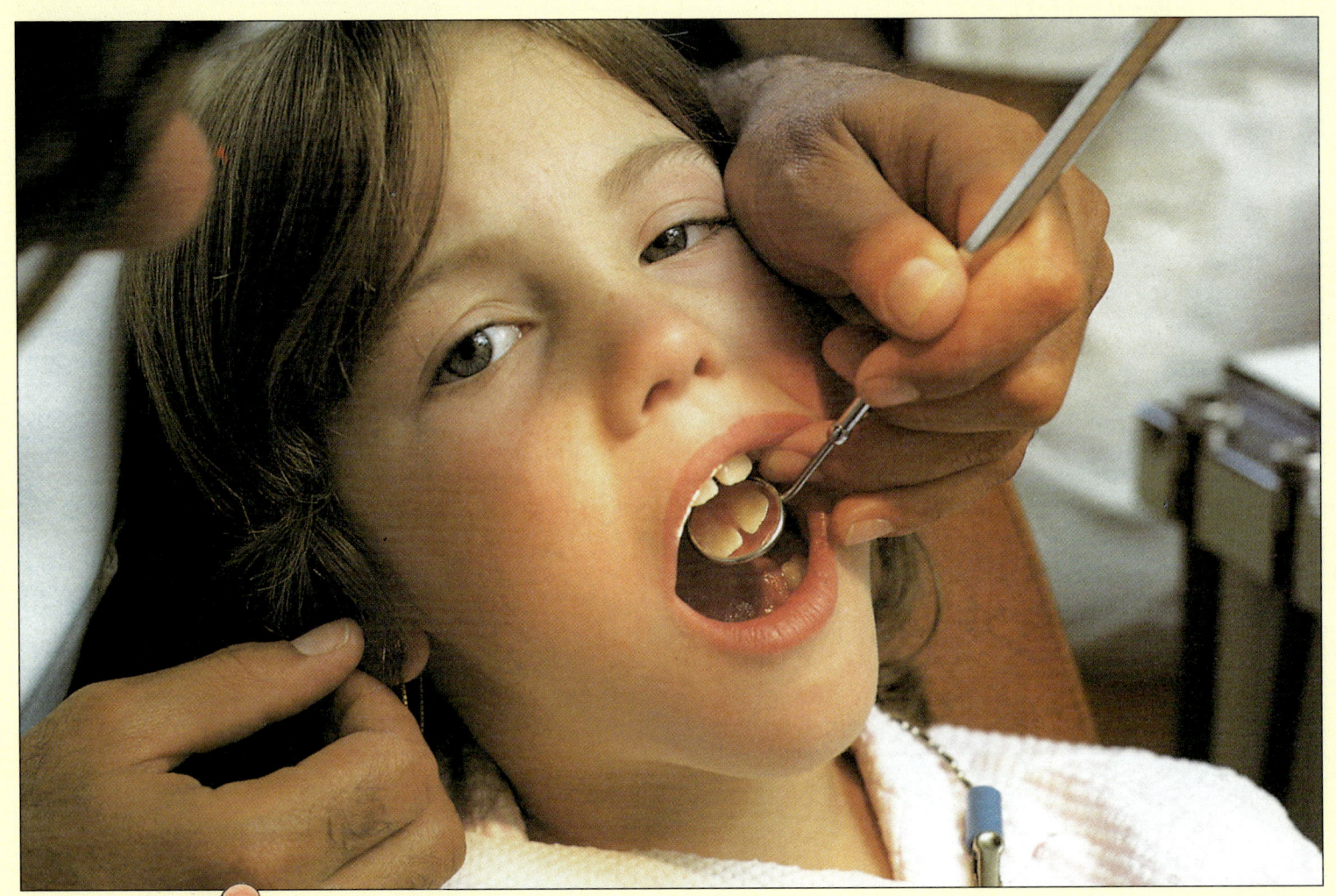

A Davinder likes to go to pop concerts but often can't see because he is too small. *Invent* something to help him see over the taller people. ◄

Q1 Draw a diagram of your invention.

Q2 Draw lines on your diagram to show how light rays pass through it.

Q3 What changes would you have to make to your invention if you wanted to be able to see behind you?

4 Refraction

Bending light

▶ Look at these pictures. What do you think causes these effects?

Light travels in straight lines but it gets bent when it goes into different substances. This is called **refraction**. Let's investigate how light is refracted by glass.

A Put the glass block on to the paper. Draw around the block. ▲

B Shine a ray of light into the block. Mark the path of the ray with crosses. ▲

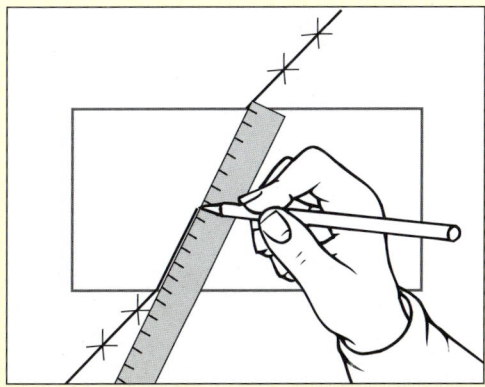

C Remove the ray box and the glass block. Draw in the rays. Connect the lines to show the path of the ray through the glass. ▲

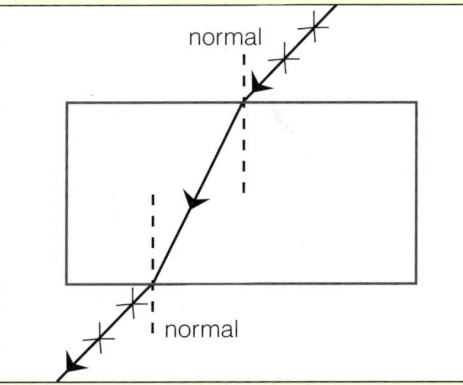

normal

normal

D Draw dotted lines at 90 degrees to the edges of the block where the ray enters and leaves the block. Each of these lines is called a **normal**. ▲

Q1 When light goes from a less dense substance (air) to a more dense substance (glass) does it bend towards or away from the normal?

Q2 How is light bent when it goes from a dense to a less dense substance (glass to air)?

Q3 Investigate what happens if you shine a ray
a at different angles to the normal.
b straight along the normal.

Extension exercise 5 can be used now.

7

Lenses

Lenses **refract** (bend) light. Lenses are usually made of glass or plastic and they have curved surfaces. There are two kinds of lenses called **convex** and **concave**.

Convex lenses are thicker in the middle than at the edges. They make light rays **converge** (bend in).

Concave lenses are thinner in the middle than at the edges. They make light rays **diverge** (bend out).

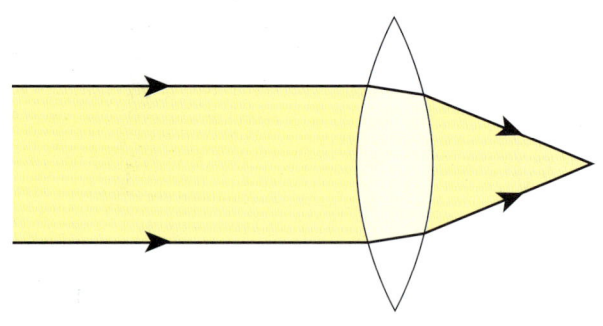

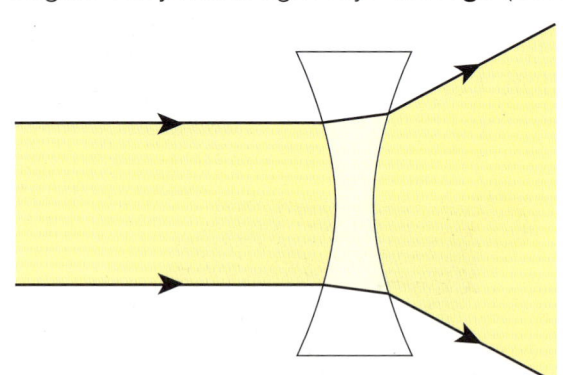

Images from convex lenses

You are now going to use convex lenses to form images.

Q1 Copy this table.

Apparatus

☐ 2 convex lenses, one fat and one thin ☐ ruler ☐ white screen

A Stand near a window. Hold the fat lens in front of the screen. Move it backwards and forwards until you see an image on the screen. ▲

B Measure how far the lens is from the screen. Record this in the table. ▲

C Repeat **A** and **B** using the thin lens.

Q2 Which forms an image nearer the lens – the thin or the fat lens?

Q3 There are many things which use lenses. Make a list of as many as you can.

Extension exercise 6 can be used now.

5 Total internal reflection

Apparatus

- ☐ ray box ☐ power pack ☐ ruler
- ☐ semicircular glass block
- ☐ protractor ☐ plain paper

▶ This ray of light bends away from the normal as it leaves the glass block. Predict what would happen if angle i was made bigger.

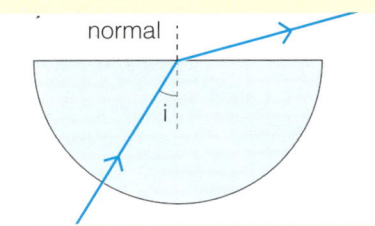

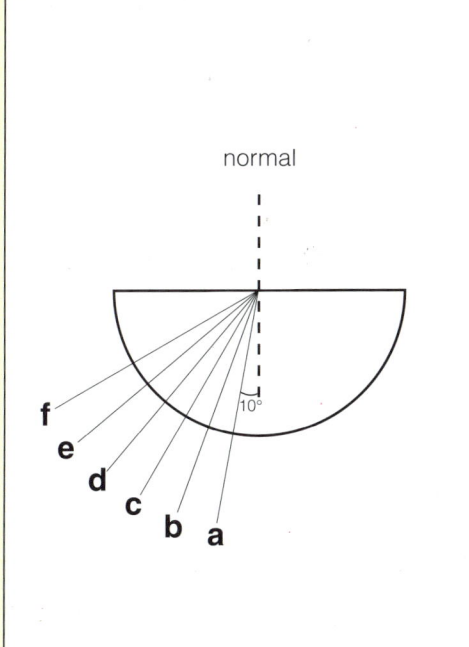

A Place the glass block on the paper and draw around it. Mark the centre of the straight side and draw a normal. ▲

B Draw lines with angles of incidence of 10°, 20°, 30°, 40°, 50° and 60°. Label these lines a, b, c, d, e and f. ▲

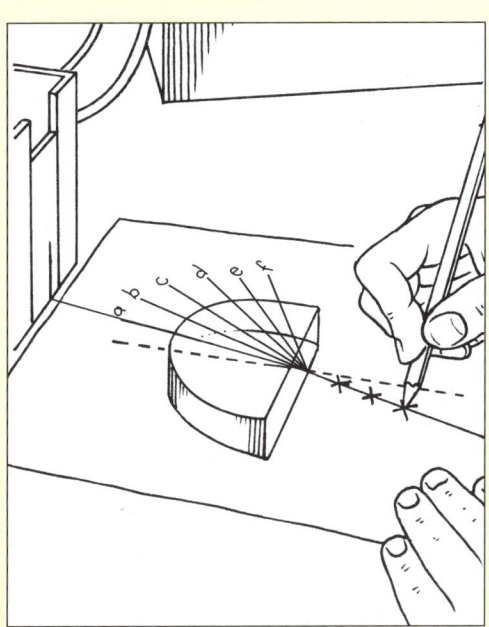

C Shine a ray along line a. Mark what happens to the ray. Do this for each of the lines. ▲

Q1 What did you predict would happen when you increased angle i?

Q2 Was your prediction correct?

Q3 Why didn't the ray bend as it went into the glass?

Q4 Describe what happened as you increased angle i.

Q5 Find the angle i at which the ray comes out along the edge of the block. This is called the **critical angle**.

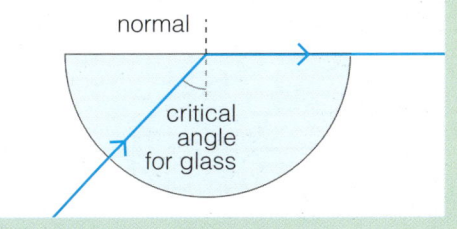

Q6 Copy and complete this passage using the words in brackets. Total internal reflection only happens when: (a) light goes from a _____ substance to a _____ substance (b) the _____ is bigger than the _____. (more dense, critical angle, less dense, angle of incidence)

Q7 Plan and, if you have time, carry out an investigation to find out if the law of reflection is true for totally internally reflected light (the angle of incidence = the angle of reflection).

Extension exercise 7 can be used now.

Optical fibres

▶ An optical fibre is a very thin, bendy strand of glass. Light reflects back and forward inside the fibre. This means that light can travel along the fibre. The fibre is covered by another layer of less dense glass which reflects the light back into the fibre.

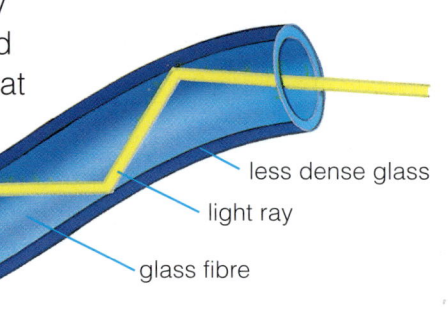

less dense glass
light ray
glass fibre

A Hold one end of the fibre close to the bulb. Look at the other end of the fibre. ▲

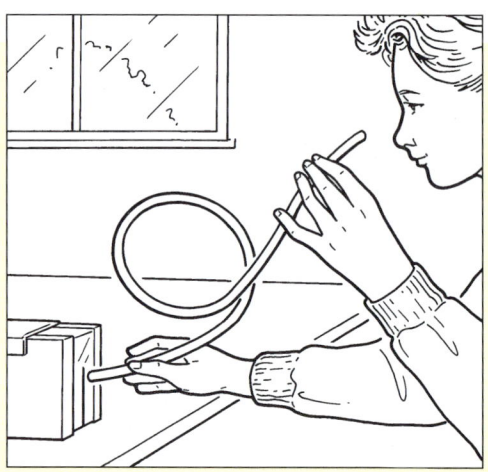

B Let's investigate if light can travel along a bent optical fibre. ▲

Apparatus

☐ optical fibre ☐ ray box
☐ power pack

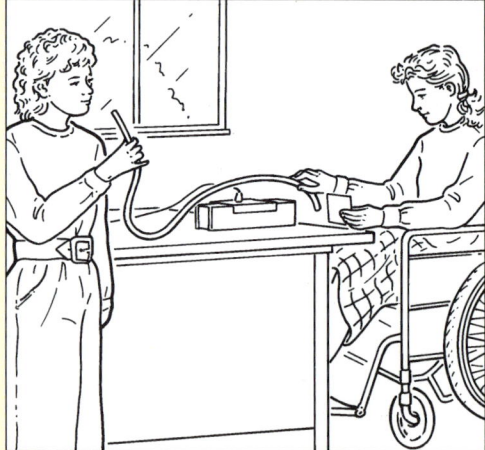

C Find a way of sending a message along the fibre to a partner. ▲

Q1 What did you see when you held the fibre close to the bulb?

Q2 Can light travel along a bent fibre?

Q3 Draw a diagram to show light travelling in a bent fibre.

Q4 Why does the outside glass have to be less dense than the inside glass?

Q5 Write down some other ways optical fibres can be used.

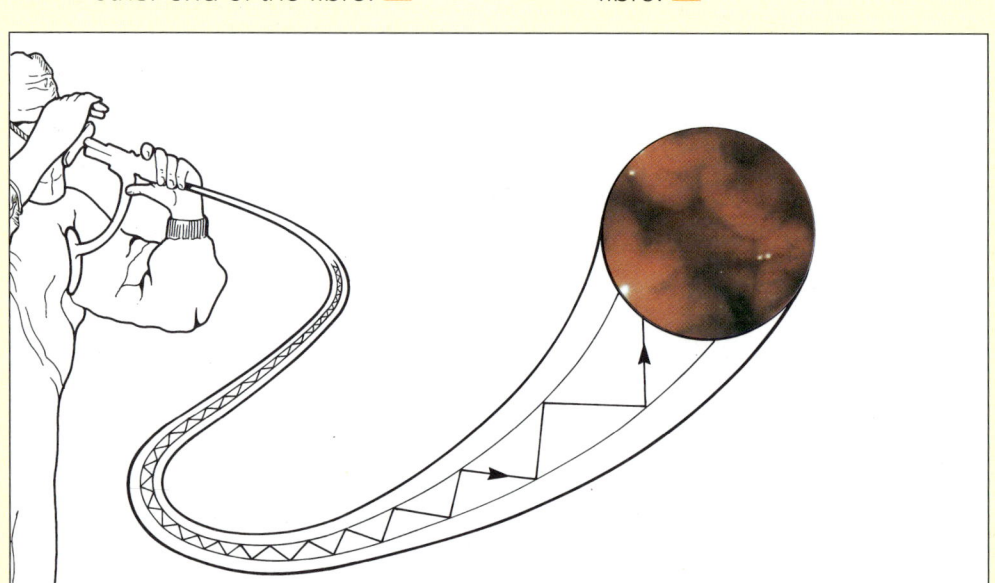

▲ Doctors use optical fibres to look inside patients' bodies without the need for surgery. They use a device called an **endoscope**. This uses optical fibres to send light into the patient's body and allow the doctor to see what is there. The endoscope can also have laser cutting equipment which allows doctors to do some operations through a small hole.

Communicating using optical fibres

▶ The idea of using light to send messages is not new. However it has some problems. It depends on the weather and, as light travels in straight lines, there must be nothing in the way. Optical fibres don't have these problems.

Light conversation

All our telephone calls used to be carried as electrical signals in copper wires. These are being replaced by fibre optic cables carrying light signals. Over 90% of Britain's long distance calls use optical fibres so you have probably used them.

▶ The transmitter turns the sound into a series of flashes of laser light. These pass along the fibre. The receiver turns the light pulses back into sound. Optical fibres can be used to send all sorts of information. Computers communicate with each other using them.

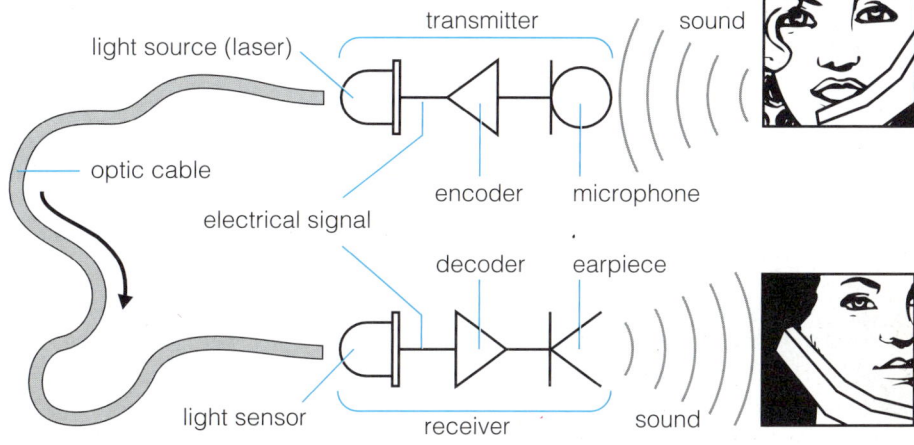

Advantages of optical fibres

■ An optical fibre as thin as a human hair can carry more than 2000 telephone calls at once. The copper wire needed to do this would be much thicker and heavier. This optical fibre cable can replace the large bundle of copper wires. Optical fibre cables are thinner and lighter than copper cables and so are easier and cheaper to install.

■ Glass is made from sand which is cheaper and more plentiful than copper.

■ The signal is carried by light not electricity. This means it is not affected by electric power lines, machinery or thunderstorms which can cause interference on old telephone lines. It is very difficult to 'tap' an optical fibre telephone line.

Q1 Design an information leaflet for British Telecom to send to customers explaining what optical fibres are and why they are being used in our telephone system.

6 Waves

Apparatus

☐ Slinky spring, one link marked with tape

Transverse and longitudinal waves

▶ Waves move energy from one place to another. Let's use a 'slinky' spring to investigate waves.

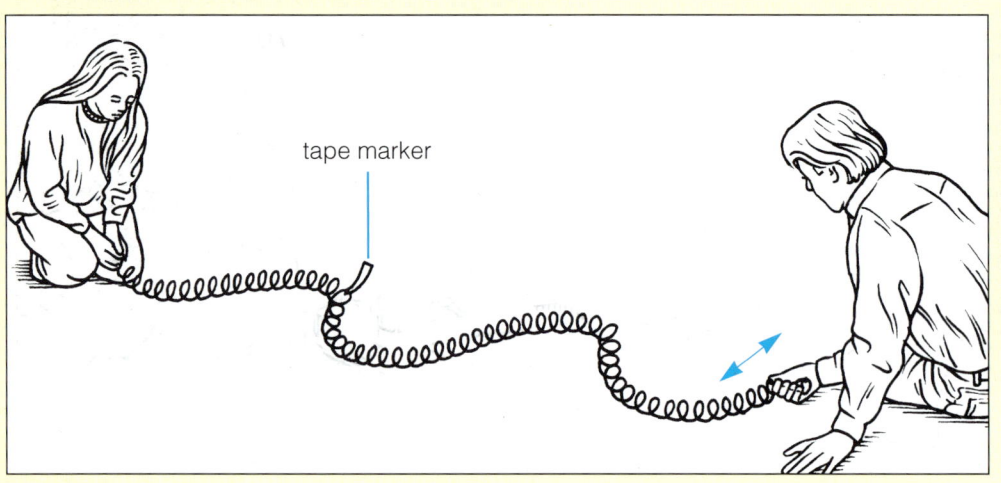

tape marker

A Work with a partner. Stretch the spring along the floor. Hold one end still. Give the other end a quick wiggle at right angles to the spring. This will make a wave move along the spring. Watch how the tape moves. This is called a **transverse wave**. Water waves and light waves are transverse waves. ▲

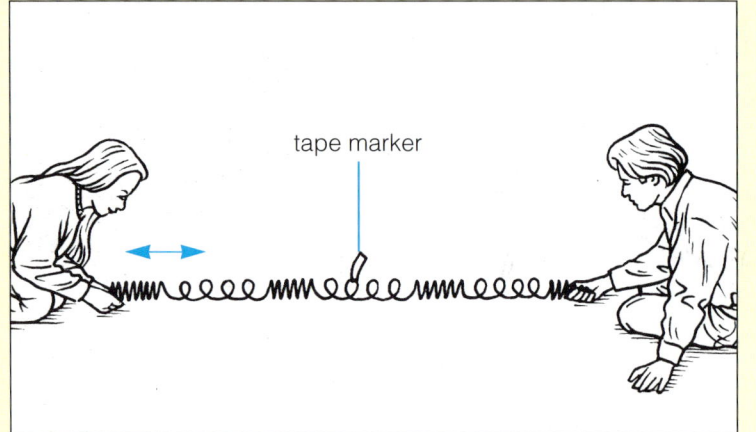

tape marker

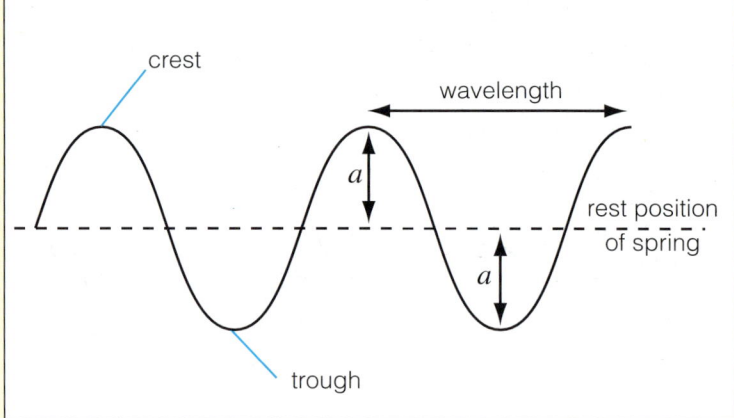

crest

wavelength

a

rest position of spring

a

trough

B Now make a different kind of wave by quickly moving the end of the spring forwards and backwards. Watch what happens to the tape. This is called a **longitudinal wave**. Sound waves are longitudinal. ▲

A transverse wave is made up of high parts (**crests**) and low parts (**troughs**). The **amplitude** a is the height of a crest above the middle, or you can measure the depth of a trough. The **wavelength** is the distance from one crest to the next. The **frequency** of the waves is the number of waves made each second. ▲

Q1 Describe how the tape marker moved in the transverse wave.

Q2 Describe how the tape marker moved in the longitudinal wave.

Q3 What happens to the waves when they hit the fixed end of the spring?

Reflection of water waves

A ripple tank is a shallow tank for looking at water waves. A bar with a motor attached makes waves in the water. The frequency of the waves can be changed by changing the speed of the motor.

A Pour water in to the tank until it is about 8–10 mm deep. Check that the tank is level so that the water is the same depth in all parts of the tank. ▲

B Adjust the bar so it is just touching the water. ▲

C Turn on the light and motor. Slowly turn up the speed of the motor. Watch the screen to see what happens to the waves. ▲

D Place a straight barrier in the tank so that the waves hit it and are reflected. ▲

Q1 Copy and complete this bird's eye view of the tank to show how the waves are reflected.

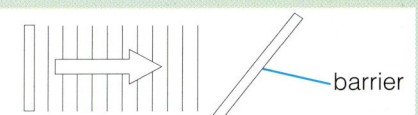

Q2 What happened to the wavelength of the waves when you increased the frequency?

Q3 What do you notice about the angle of incidence of the waves and the angle of reflection?

Refraction of water waves

Apparatus

☐ ripple tank ☐ power pack
☐ bar ☐ motor ☐ light
☐ Perspex sheet
☐ large sheet of white paper

▶ Waves can change direction as they go into shallow water. Refraction happens because the waves move more slowly in shallow water.

A Put the Perspex sheet into the tank. Adjust the water level so the sheet is covered by about 2 mm of water. Switch on the motor and watch what happens to the waves. ▲

B Move the sheet so that the waves enter the shallow water at an angle. Watch what happens as the waves go into the shallow water. ▲

Q1 What happens to the waves when they go into shallow water? Explain why this happens.

Q2 Copy and complete these bird's eye views of the tank to show how water waves are refracted.

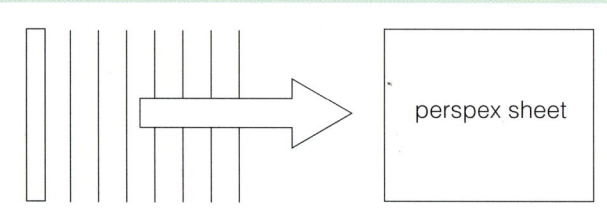

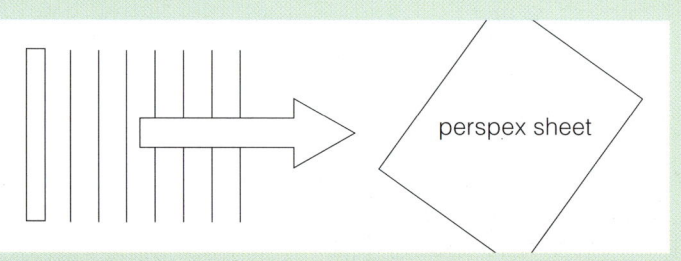

Extension exercise 8 can be used now.

7 Colours of light

Apparatus

☐ ray box ☐ power pack
☐ prism ☐ white screen
☐ coloured pencils

Making a spectrum

Light is made up of lots of colours. A **prism** bends the light and splits it into these colours.

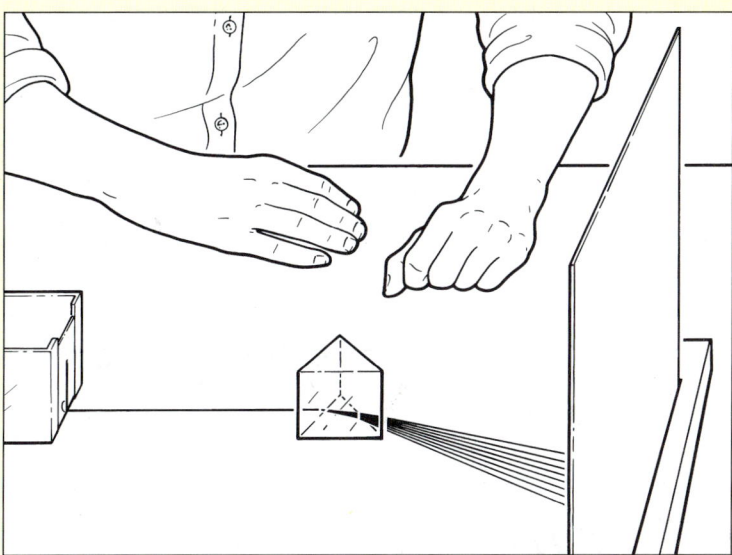

A Shine white light through the prism onto the screen. ▲

B Turn the prism until you can see a band of colours on the screen. This is called a **spectrum**. ▲

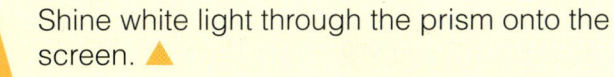

red

orange

yellow

green

blue

indigo

violet

◀ Sunlight is white light. It contains all the colours of the spectrum. A rainbow is made when raindrops act as little prisms and split up the colours.

Q1 Use coloured pencils to draw your spectrum.

Q2 Which colour of light is bent most by a prism?

Q3 Which colour of light is bent least by a prism?

Q4 What must the weather be like for a rainbow to form?

Waves and radiation

If you threw a stone into a pond you would see ripples (**waves**) spreading out from it.

▶ Light spreads out in the same way. It travels as a wave.

▶ These waves are different lengths for the different colours of light.

The spectrum of light we can see is just a small part of a bigger spectrum called the **electromagnetic spectrum**. This is made up of a lot of different types of **radiation**.

All these types of radiation behave like light.

They all travel at the same speed in air, which is 300 million metres per second.

They can all be reflected and refracted.

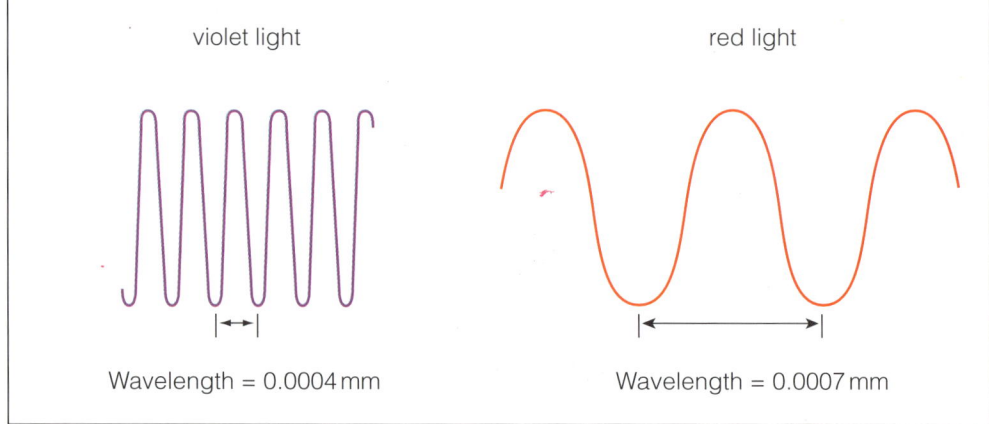

violet light — Wavelength = 0.0004 mm

red light — Wavelength = 0.0007 mm

▼ Heat radiated by the sun can be brought to a hot focus by a lens.

▼ The heat radiated by the element of an electric fire is reflected forwards by the curved shiny metal behind.

▼ The concave dish of this radio telescope reflects radio waves from space onto a receiver at its centre.

Q1 What is different about the different types of waves in the electromagnetic spectrum?

Q2 At what speed do all types of electromagnetic radiation travel in air?

Electromagnetic waves

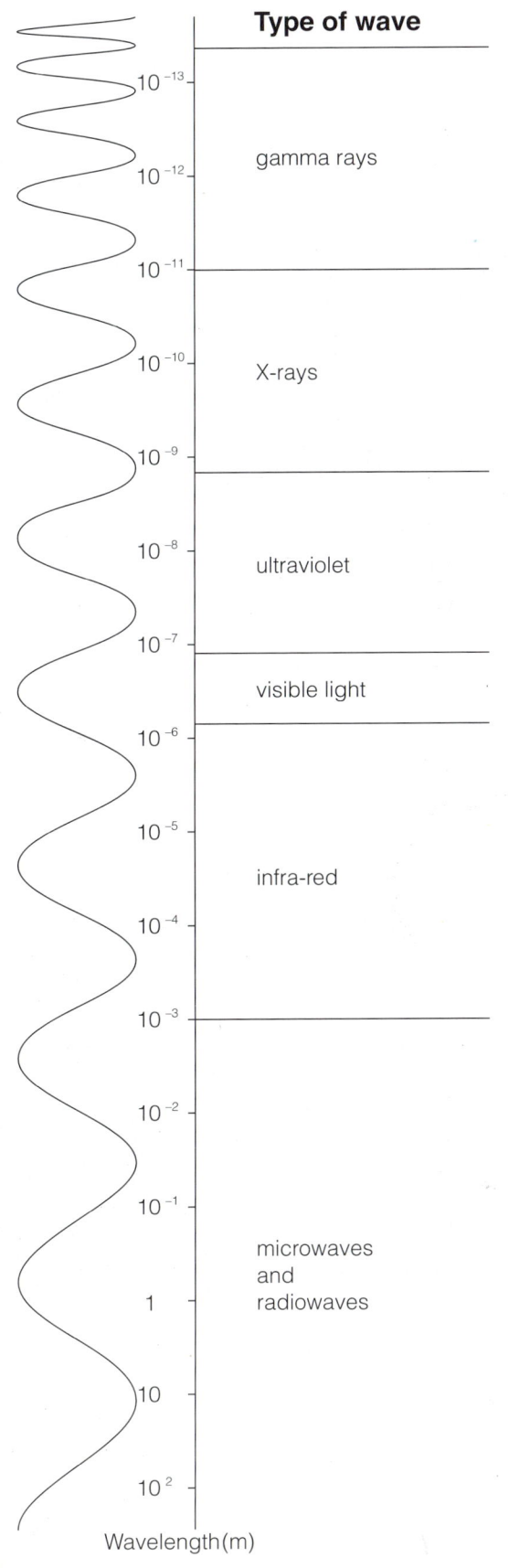

Type of wave

Wavelength(m)	
10^{-13}	
10^{-12}	gamma rays
10^{-11}	
10^{-10}	X-rays
10^{-9}	
10^{-8}	ultraviolet
10^{-7}	
10^{-6}	visible light
10^{-5}	
10^{-4}	infra-red
10^{-3}	
10^{-2}	
10^{-1}	
1	microwaves and radiowaves
10	
10^2	

Wavelength(m)

Where do waves come from?

▶ Gamma rays are produced in the sun, stars and nuclear reactions.

▶ X-rays are produced by special high energy machinery.

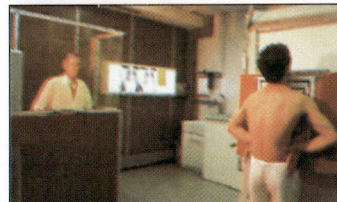

▶ Ultraviolet rays are produced by very hot objects.

▶ Visible light is produced by hot objects and fluorescent (glowing) materials.

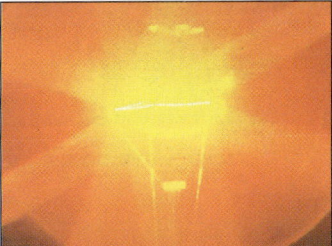

▶ Anything which is warmer than its surroundings produces infra-red radiation.

▶ Special electrical circuits are used to produce microwaves and radio waves.

9 Using electromagnetic waves

Waves in the home

Electromagnetic waves are used in many areas of our lives, including in our homes.

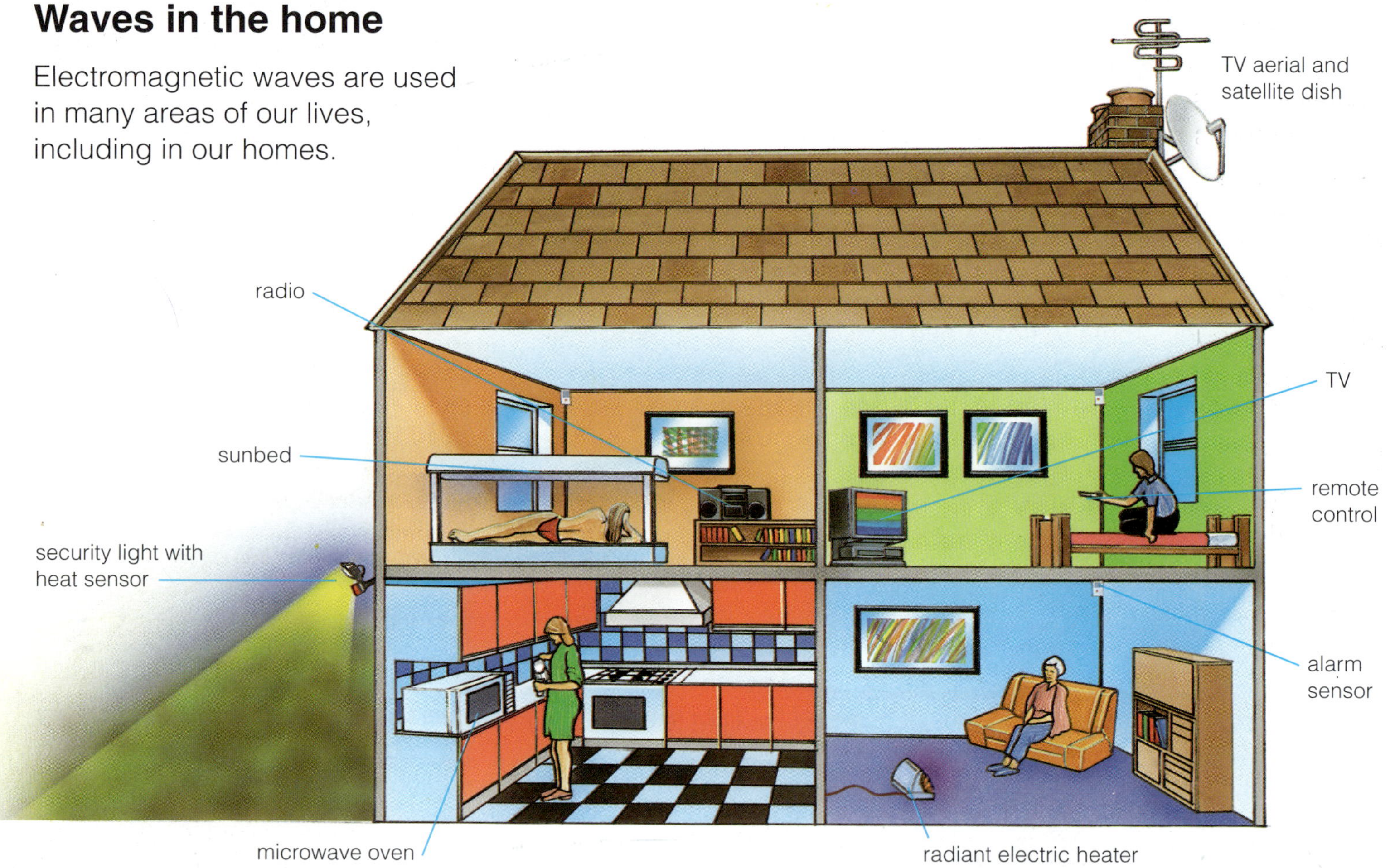

TV aerial and satellite dish

radio

sunbed

TV

remote control

security light with heat sensor

alarm sensor

microwave oven

radiant electric heater

▲ Microwaves

Microwaves cook food very quickly. Foods containing water absorb (take in) the energy of the microwaves. This makes the particles in the food move very fast and so the food gets very hot.

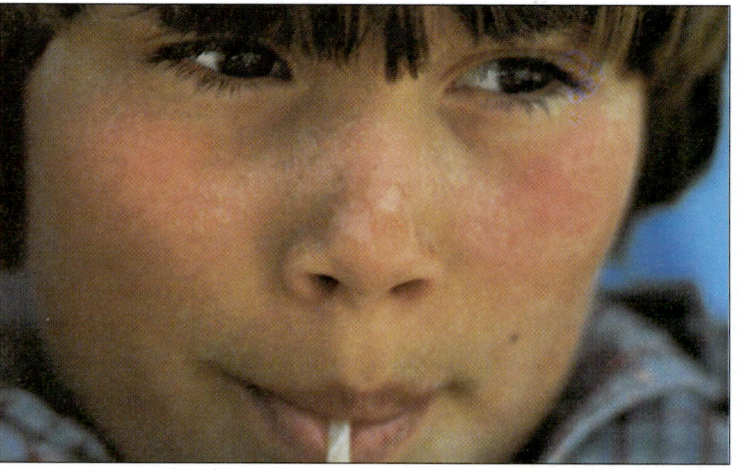

▲ Ultraviolet radiation

Ultraviolet radiation from the sun or from sun lamps causes tanning. In large amounts these rays can cause severe burning and sometimes skin cancer. This can be reduced by using creams to block out the harmful rays. However it is safer not to stay out in strong sunlight for too long, or not to go out in it at all.

Infra-red burglar alarms

▶ Many burglar alarms include **passive infra-red detectors**. These detect heat radiation from moving objects. The detector contains two infra-red sensors. In front of the sensors is a curved piece of plastic containing lenses which focus the radiation onto the sensors. As an intruder moves across the room, his body heat is detected by the two sensors in turn. This gives a changing signal which sets off the alarm. Continuous heat, such as sunlight, does not affect the alarm.

These detectors are also used outdoors to switch on bright security lights to scare off burglars.

▶ Televisions, videos and music systems can be controlled by infra-red rays. A remote control unit sends a series of infra-red rays which control the volume, change channel, etc. A different pattern of rays is used for each command.

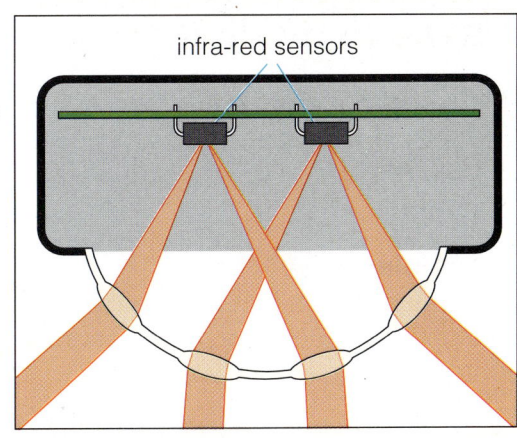
infra-red sensors

Apparatus

- [ ] light bulb in stand
- [ ] clamp
- [ ] low energy light bulb
- [ ] stand
- [ ] heat sensitive paper
- [ ] thermometer with blackened bulb

Take care, light bulbs can get very hot

A Hold the heat sensitive paper close to the bulb. Note what happens. ▲

B Clamp the thermometer close to the unlit bulb. Record the temperature. Switch on the bulb and record how the temperature changes. ▲

C Investigate the amount of heat radiation produced by the low energy bulb and that produced by the ordinary bulb. Be sure to make it a fair test.

Q1 How did the amount of heat energy produced by the low energy bulb compare to that produced by the ordinary bulb?

Q2 Which bulb do you think uses less electrical energy?

Q3 Make a list of all the uses of electromagnetic waves in our homes. For example, microwaves are used for cooking.

Use	Type of radiation
Cooking	Microwaves

Q4 What kinds of waves do lamps give out?

Q5 Which produces more infra-red – an ordinary bulb or a low energy bulb?

Waves in medicine

Many types of electromagnetic waves are used by doctors. Care must be taken because they can be harmful if they are not used properly.

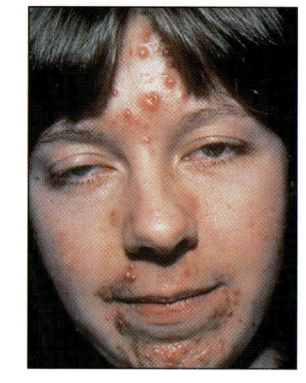
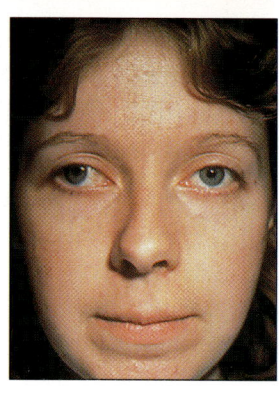

Ultraviolet light

▶ Ultraviolet rays can be used to treat some skin problems. This patient's acne has been treated with drugs and a controlled amount of UV light.

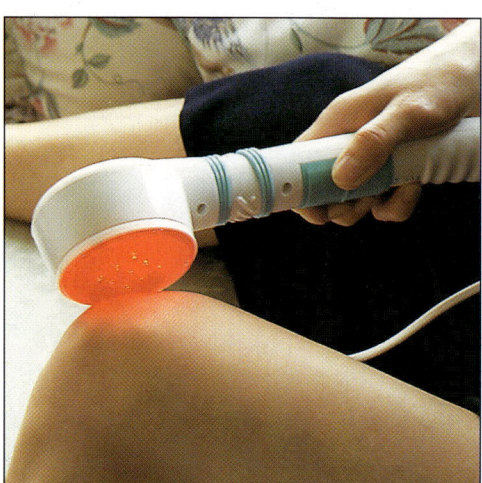

Infra-red light

◀ Some injuries, such as sprains, heal faster if they are heated. The infra-red lamp heats the damaged tissues and this makes more blood flow to speed up healing.

X-Rays

▶ X-rays can pass through soft tissues in our bodies but not through bones. They can be used to photograph bones. X-rays can be harmful if you are exposed to too many. Pregnant women should avoid X-rays because the developing baby can be damaged by them.

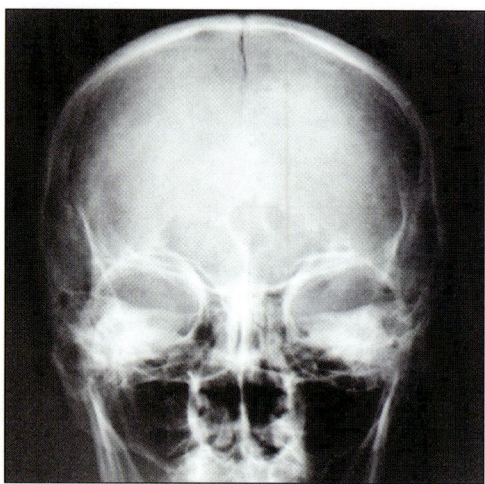

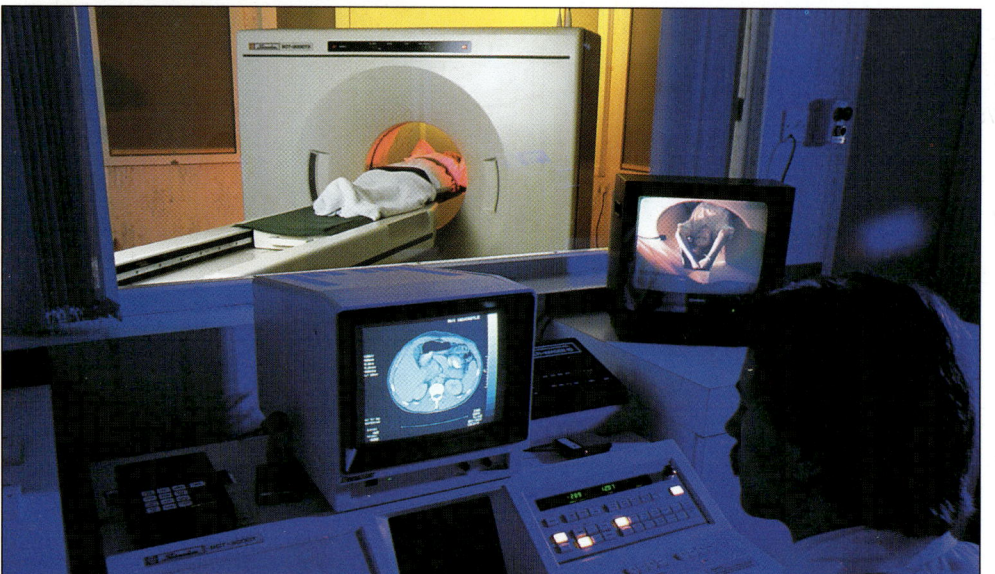

◀ Normal X-ray photos give a flat picture. When more information is needed, doctors use a CAT (computerized axial tomography) scanner. This takes X-ray pictures from many directions. A computer is used to make these into a three-dimensional picture of the patient.

Q1 Which health problems can be helped using ultraviolet light?

Q2 Name two sources of UV light

Q3 Why must the amount of UV light used be carefully controlled?

Q4 How are infra-red lamps used for injuries?

Q5 Why should pregnant women avoid X-rays?

Q6 Why is a CAT scanner sometimes more useful than an ordinary X-ray picture?

Gamma rays

Gamma rays are dangerous. They can damage cells in our bodies, causing cancer and many other problems. However, for people with cancer, if they are used carefully, they can kill damaged cells and stop the cancer spreading.

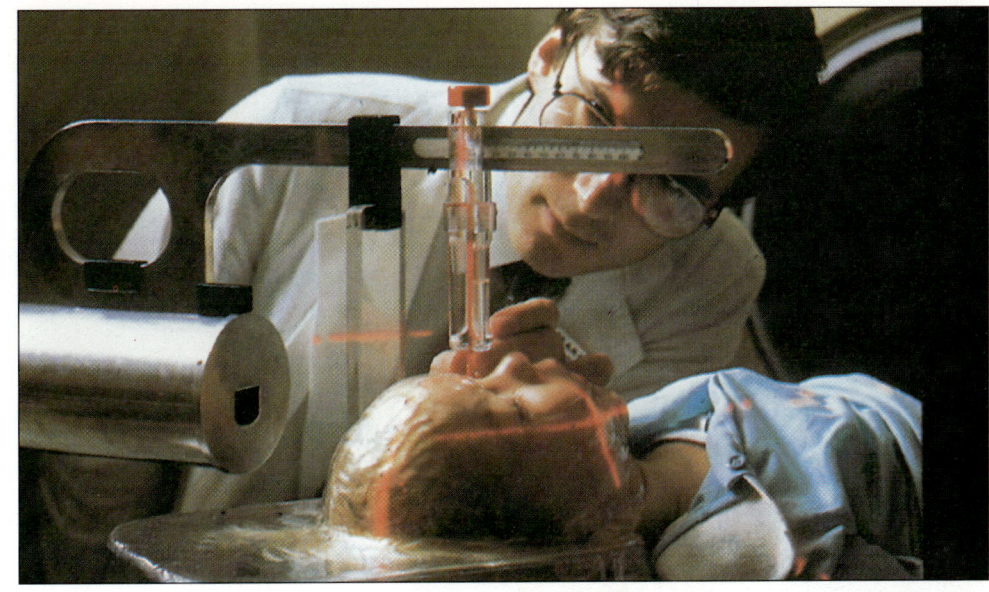

▲ The red light is used to help direct the gamma rays.

◄ Rays are directed at the tumour from different directions. Only the tumour is irradiated (hit by the rays) each time so healthy cells are not damaged. X-rays can also be used like this.

tumour

▶ Gamma rays can be used to detect problems. For example, to check if a patient's kidneys are working properly a chemical which gives out gamma rays is injected into the patient. Doctors can detect the gamma rays and find out where the chemical has got to. If the kidneys are working properly they pass the chemical to the bladder. If a lot of the chemical stays in the kidneys, the doctor knows there is a problem.

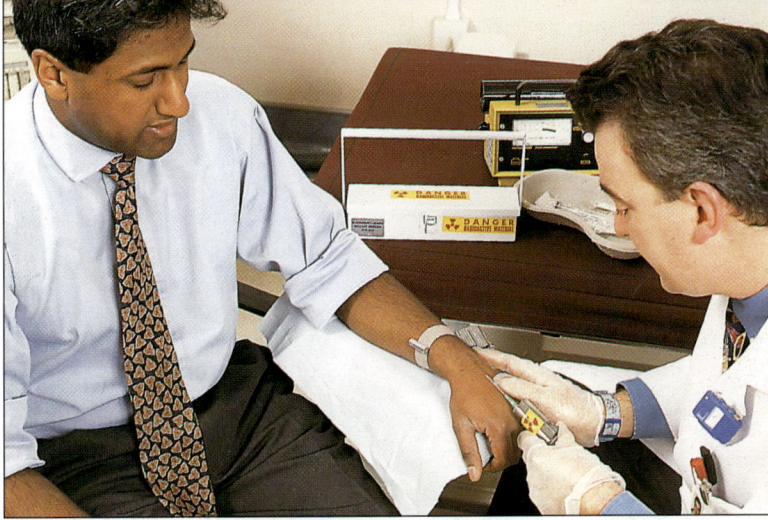

▶ Gamma rays kill bacteria. Equipment is sealed in plastic then irradiated. This sterilises the equipment.

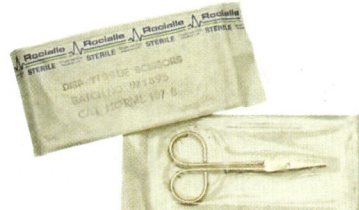

Q1 Describe how a cancerous growth can be treated with gamma rays.

Q2 Why is equipment sealed in plastic before it is irradiated?

Q3 Design a poster for a hospital waiting room telling patients about all the uses of electromagnetic waves. Explain why they must be used with care.

Extension exercise 9 can be used now.

Communicating using waves

▶ Radio and television broadcasts are carried by radio waves of different wavelengths. They are detected by aerials and the TV set changes them back into sounds and pictures.

Telecommunications towers

◀ These use short wavelength microwaves to receive and transmit TV signals and telephone conversations. The microwaves can be made into a powerful beam carrying lots of information. The towers have to be tall so nothing blocks the beam. Many towers are needed to carry messages around the Earth's curved surface.

Satellites

▶ Satellites orbit high above the Earth. Microwave beams are sent up to them. Satellites contain electronic equipment to make the signal stronger and send it back to Earth. Signals can be sent all around the world in this way.

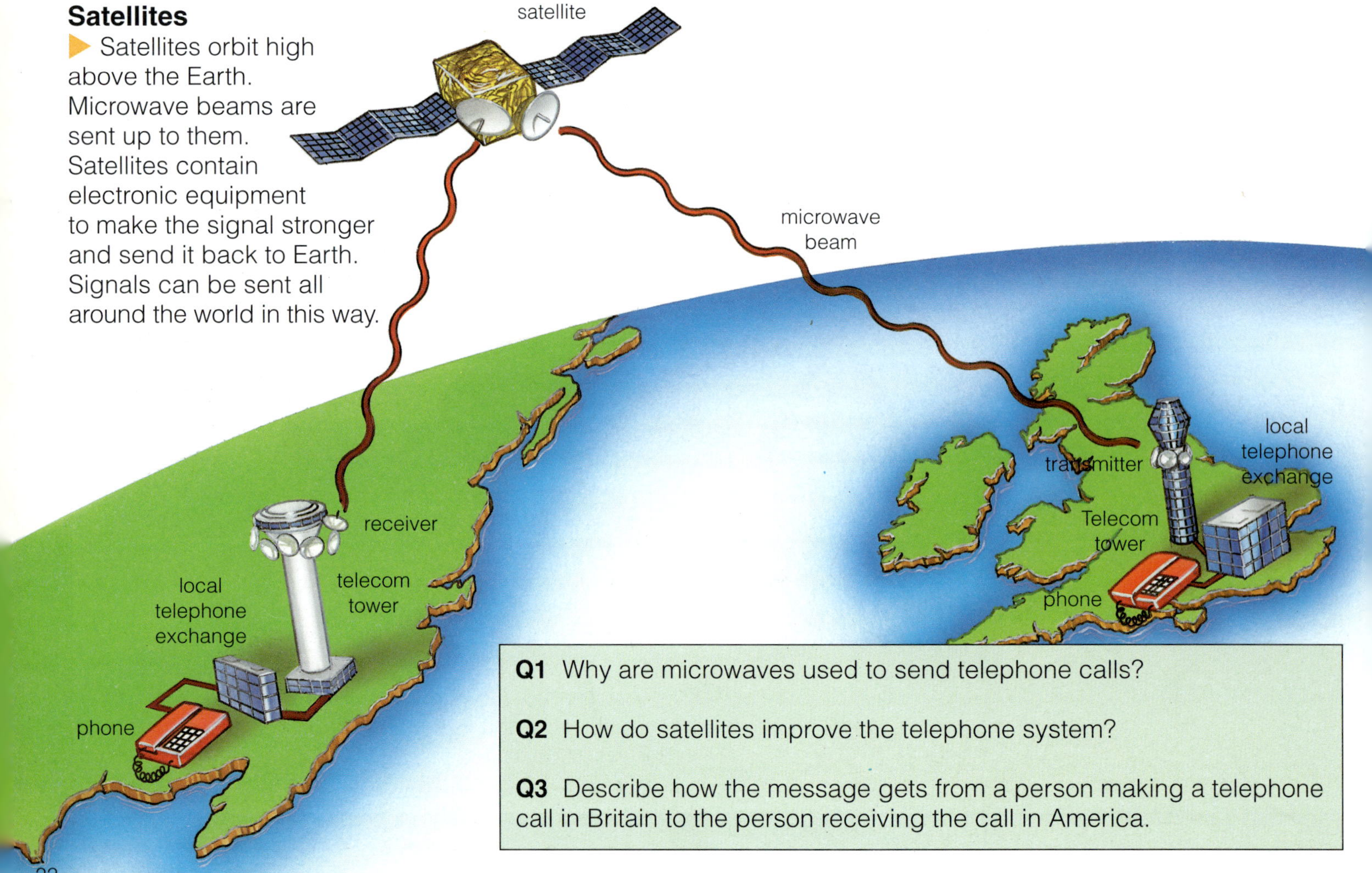

satellite

microwave beam

receiver

local telephone exchange

telecom tower

phone

transmitter

local telephone exchange

Telecom tower

phone

Q1 Why are microwaves used to send telephone calls?

Q2 How do satellites improve the telephone system?

Q3 Describe how the message gets from a person making a telephone call in Britain to the person receiving the call in America.

Cellular telephones

▶ Mobile telephones use high frequency radio waves. The telephone companies divide countries into areas called cells. Each cell has a base station which receives and transmits calls. If a call is to a different cell, the message is sent to a central control station. This sends the message to the other cell by microwaves or along optical fibres. It is then changed back to a radio signal to be picked up by a telephone.

▼ In cities, where there are lots of people and so lots of telephones, the cells are small. In country areas they are bigger. The radius of a cell can vary from 200 metres to 35 kilometres.

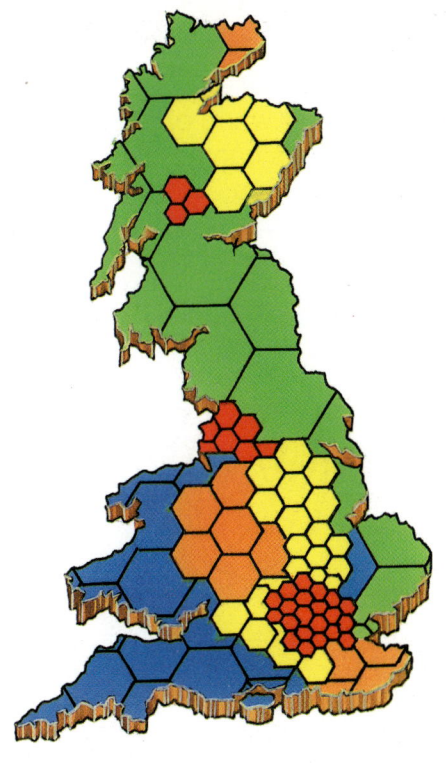

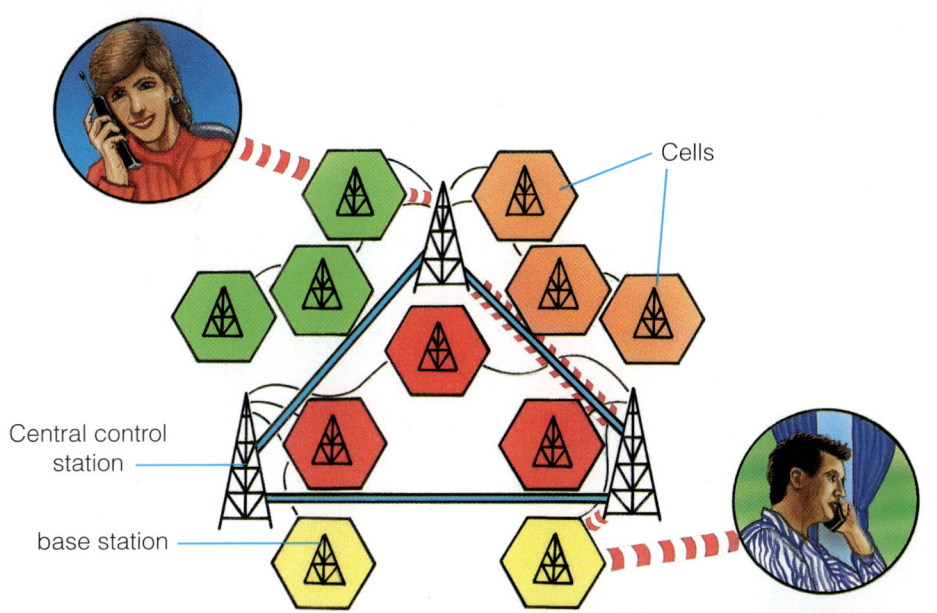

Cells

Central control station

base station

Pictures from space

◀ For thousands of years, we have looked at the stars. New technology helps us to detect *all* the waves coming from space, not just the visible light. All the waves in the spectrum can travel through the vacuum of space, but some are stopped by our atmosphere. Satellite telescopes and cameras outside our atmosphere pick up radiation from space. This gives us better information from the stars.

Q1 Why are cells bigger in country areas than in cities?

Q2 Describe the path of the signal when a mobile telephone user calls someone in a different cell. You can draw a diagram if it helps.

Q3 Why can telescopes on satellites give us more information than telescopes on Earth?

Seeing the invisible

Infra-red

▼ Any hot or warm object gives out infra-red radiation. This can be detected using a special heat sensitive camera.

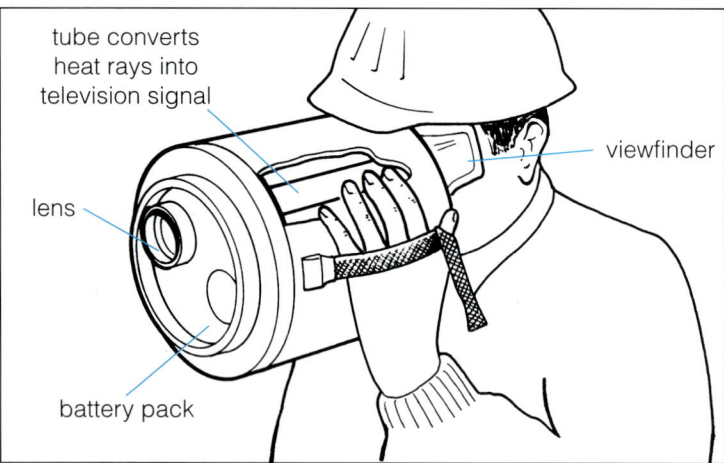

tube converts heat rays into television signal

viewfinder

lens

battery pack

► After an earthquake, people may be trapped under the rubble. As their bodies are warm they can be detected using infra-red photography.

Ultraviolet

◄ Ultraviolet light can be used to check if bank notes are forged. Most paper is treated with chemicals to make it bright. This makes the paper glow (fluoresce) in ultraviolet light. Bank notes are made of paper which isn't treated with these chemicals so real notes look the same in ultraviolet light as they do in normal light.

Q1 How can infra-red photography help to save lives?

Q2 Think of any other ways these cameras could be used.

Q3 How do banks use ultraviolet light?

Q4 Which bank note is forged?